ADVENTURES WITH ELECTRONICS

TOM DUNCAN

JOHN MURRAY

Acknowledgements

Thanks are due to John, Nicola, David, Howard, Brian, Heather, Fred, Dave, Penny, Arthur and Freda for checking circuits, taking photographs or giving other help with the preparation of the book.

First published 1978
by John Murray (Publishers) Ltd
50 Albemarle Street, London W1X 4BD

Reprinted 1979, 1980, 1985, 1987, 1990, 1991, 1993, 1996

Printed in Hong Kong by
Wing King Tong Co., Ltd.

0 7195 3554 9

ADVENTURES WITH ELECTRONICS

Contents

HOW
TO
START

THIS WAY UP

Use a complete 'Adventures with Electronics' kit or get the parts separately (see page 58).

You will also need: *pliers* for cutting wire and removing plastic insulation from its ends, *scissors* for cutting insulating sleeving, a *penknife* for scraping dirt off the ends of wires to be connected and a *small screwdriver*.

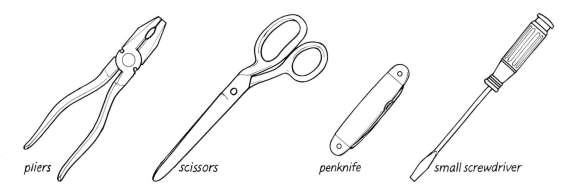

pliers   scissors   penknife   small screwdriver

Before tackling any of the projects it is best to work through pages 2 to 8. This will make you familiar with the bits and pieces used in electronic circuits and give you confidence to launch out on the projects.

THE BITS AND PIECES

PART	CIRCUIT SIGN	WHAT IT DOES

Battery ($4\frac{1}{2}$ = 4.5 volt, type 126)

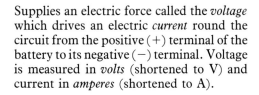

Supplies an electric force called the *voltage* which drives an electric *current* round the circuit from the positive (+) terminal of the battery to its negative (−) terminal. Voltage is measured in *volts* (shortened to V) and current in *amperes* (shortened to A).

Lamp and holder
(6 volt 0.06 ampere)

Produces light and heat when current passes through the filament (a short metal wire) and makes it white hot.

Connecting wire (tinned copper, 22 gauge)

wires connected

wires not connected

Allows current to flow through it easily because it is made of copper which is a good electrical conductor. Insulators like rubber, plastic and enamel do not allow current to pass through them and are used to cover bare wires.

Resistor (carbon, $\frac{1}{2}$ watt)

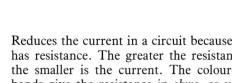

Reduces the current in a circuit because it has resistance. The greater the resistance the smaller is the current. The coloured bands give the resistance in *ohms*, as you will see shortly.

Potentiometer
(10 kilohm, linear)

Varies the resistance between the centre terminal and the end terminals when the spindle is rotated. Resistance value between the end terminals is marked on the case.

PART	CIRCUIT SIGN	WHAT IT DOES

Photocell or **light dependent resistor** (e.g. ORP12)

When light falls on it, its resistance becomes low; in the dark its resistance is high.

Thermistor or **temperature dependent resistor** (e.g. TH3)

When heated, its resistance gets smaller; when cooled, its resistance increases.

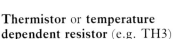

Capacitor (ceramic type)

Stores electricity; the greater the capacitance the more does it store. Capacitance values are measured in microfarads shortened to μF or, less correctly, to mfd. On a capacitor, $0.1\,\mu$F may be marked as .1 mfd and $0.01\,\mu$F as 10 n. The greatest voltage it can stand is also shown, e.g. 30 V.

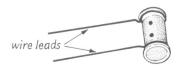

Electrolytic capacitor

Stores electricity: values usually larger than $1\,\mu$F. Greatest voltage marked on it. *Must be connected the correct way round.*

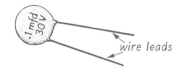

Variable capacitor (0.0005 microfarads)

Varies the capacitance in a circuit by moving one set of metal plates in or out of a fixed set when the spindle is rotated. The sets of plates are separated by sheets of an insulator (also called a dielectric).

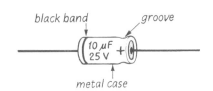

Diode (OA91)

Lets current flow in one direction but not in the other. The arrow on the sign and the band on the diode, show the conducting direction.

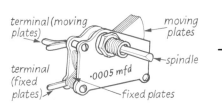

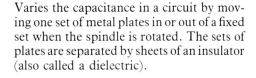

3

PART	CIRCUIT SIGN	WHAT IT DOES

Transistors

WHAT IT DOES

A transistor acts as a very fast switch.

1 *npn type* (2N3053 or BFY51)

2N 3053 —metal case
tag
c b e

collector c
base b
emitter e

It amplifies small currents into much larger copies.

It must be *correctly connected* or it will be damaged so you have to know which of the three leads is which in each type. In a 2N3053 and a BFY51, which have metal cases, the *emitter* is nearest the tag on the case and the *collector* is connected to the case; in a ZTX500 the *emitter* can be recognized from the shape of the bottom of the case, as can the *source* in a 2N3819.

2 *pnp type* (ZTX500)

ZTX 500 —plastic case
c b e

collector c
base b
emitter e

An npn type needs a *positive collector* voltage, a pnp type needs a *negative collector* voltage so you cannot replace one type by the other (unless changes are made to the circuit). The arrow on the sign for an npn type points from the base to the emitter; it points in the opposite direction in a pnp type.

3 *field effect type* (2N3819)

2N 3819 —plastic case
d g s

drain d
gate g
source s

Integrated circuit (ZN414 or ZN414Z)

ZN 414 —metal case
tag
3 2 1
ZN 414Z
plastic case
3 2 1

2 IC 1
3

Does the jobs of several transistors, diodes, resistors and capacitors.

It must be correctly connected.

Crystal earphone

Changes electric currents into sound.

Loudspeaker (2½ inch, 25 to 80 ohms)

Changes electric currents into sound.

Ferrite rod aerial

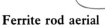

ferrite rod

enamelled copper wire

Changes radio waves into electric currents.

BUILDING S-DeC CIRCUITS

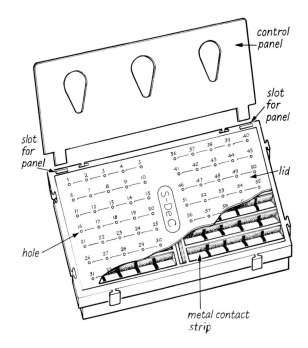

control panel

slot for panel

slot for panel

lid

metal contact strip

hole

An S-DeC is a plastic box with a lid which has seventy numbered holes. It has fourteen metal contact strips under the lid, seven on each side of the box. The strip under holes 1 to 5 automatically connects wires put into any of these holes. The strip below holes 6 to 10 connects all the wires in these and so on.

To make a connection push about 2 cm of *bare* wire *straight* into the hole (not at an angle) so that it is gripped by the contact strip.

Do not push it in too far or use wires that are *dirty* or have *kinked ends*; they could damage the contacts when pulled out.

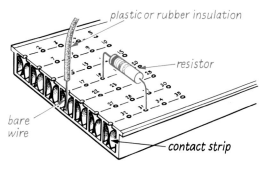

plastic or rubber insulation

resistor

bare wire

contact strip

Only put one wire in each hole.

Bend leads on resistors and other parts as shown but *do not have the bend too close* to where the wire comes out of the part or it may break off.

Do not shorten leads from parts.

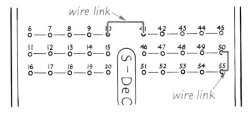

wire link

wire link

Use a wire link when two sets of holes have to be connected.

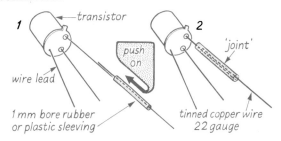

1

transistor

push on

wire lead

1 mm bore rubber or plastic sleeving

2

'joint'

tinned copper wire 22 gauge

Lengthen transistor leads by making 'joints' as shown. You will have to do this to get all three leads into holes on the S-DeC.

Wrap bare wire round and under battery and lamp holder terminals before screwing them down.
Do not over-tighten the battery terminals or the connections inside the battery can be broken.

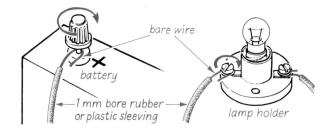

bare wire

battery

—1 mm bore rubber or plastic sleeving

lamp holder

Mount variable capacitors and potentiometers on the control panel. Connect wires to them as shown below *before* slotting the panel into the S-DeC.

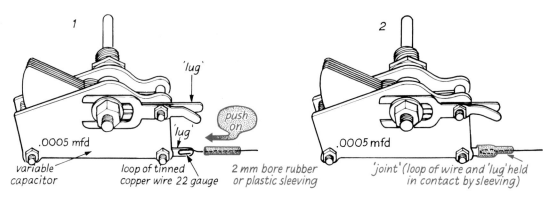

1

'lug'

push on

'lug'

.0005 mfd

variable capacitor

loop of tinned copper wire 22 gauge

2 mm bore rubber or plastic sleeving

2

.0005 mfd

'joint' (loop of wire and 'lug' held in contact by sleeving)

The centre 'lug' on a potentiometer is usually made of thinner metal than the end 'lugs' and more care is needed when making a 'joint' with it. It helps if you press your thumb against the bottom of the 'lug' so that it cannot bend when you push the sleeving over it.

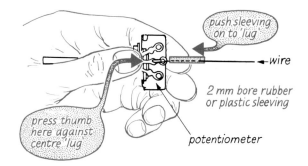

push sleeving on to 'lug'

wire

2 mm bore rubber or plastic sleeving

press thumb here against centre 'lug'

potentiometer

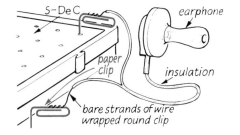

S-DeC

earphone

paper clip

insulation

bare strands of wire wrapped round clip

If you have bought the parts separately the earphone will have 'stranded' wire leads. (Those in the 'Adventures with Electronics' kit have had a single thick wire joined to them.) To connect them to the S-DeC use paper clips which have been partly opened out.

> If you follow the above instructions your S-DeC will give good service for a long time.

RESISTOR COLOUR CODE

Resistor values are given in *ohms* (shortened to Ω, the Greek letter 'omega'). They are marked on the resistor using a colour code.

Three coloured bands are painted round the resistor. Each colour stands for a number. To read the colour code, start at the 1st band; it is nearest the end. Sometimes it is not clear which is the 1st band because there is a 4th band of gold or silver near the other end. These two colours are not used for the 1st band; they give the accuracy of the resistor (gold is ± 5% and silver ±10%), so you should not have too much trouble deciding where to start.

The *1st band* gives the first number, the *2nd band* gives the second number and the *3rd band* tells how many noughts come after the first two numbers.

Number	Colour
0	black
1	brown
2	red
3	orange
4	yellow
5	green
6	blue
7	violet
8	grey
9	white

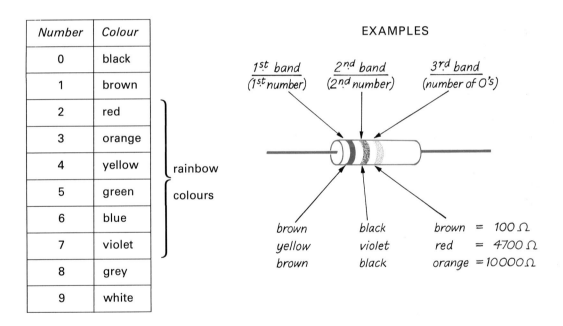

EXAMPLES

1st band (1st number)	2nd band (2nd number)	3rd band (number of 0's)	
brown	black	brown	= 100 Ω
yellow	violet	red	= 4700 Ω
brown	black	orange	=10000 Ω

More resistor shorthand

$$1000\,\Omega = 1\,\text{kilohm} = 1\,\text{k}\Omega$$
$$4700\,\Omega = 4.7\,\text{kilohm} = 4.7\,\text{k}\Omega$$
$$1\,000\,000\,\Omega = 1\,\text{megohm} = 1\,\text{M}\Omega$$

HINTS
FOR
SUCCESS

Collect all the parts you need for a project before starting it. They may not always look exactly like those shown on pages 2 to 4 but you should be able to recognize them.

Be certain about which connections are which on transistors, integrated circuits and electrolytic capacitors. They can be damaged if connected wrongly. The markings on some transistors are easily rubbed off so do not finger them any more than you need to.

After building a circuit do not connect the battery until you have

- **a** checked the circuit carefully,
- **b** made sure that bare wires, especially transistor leads, are not touching one another (or the can of the transistor if it is made of metal). If they do touch, 'short circuits' and damage may occur.

Take care to connect the battery the correct way round, as shown on the diagrams. In circuits with lamps or a loudspeaker, disconnect the battery when you are not using the circuit, otherwise it will run down.

If a circuit still does not work after careful checking it may be that a transistor has become faulty because at some time it was connected wrongly by accident. You can test it as described on page 56.

The projects are best done in the order given; you will then follow things better. Do not be tempted to rush into building a radio before doing some simpler jobs. S-DeC layouts are always given; however, after you have assembled a few successfully you may find it more fun to work out your own arrangement from the circuit diagram.

> All circuits are shown working from a 4.5 V battery but 6 V can be used instead, except that in project 13 – 'Chip' Radio – the values of two resistors have to be changed (see page 40 for details).

HAPPY PROJECTING!

1
SOME SIMPLE CIRCUITS

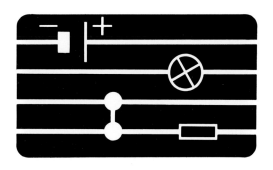

Connect the circuits using tinned copper wire (22 gauge) and cover it with 1 mm bore plastic (or rubber) sleeving to prevent 'short circuits'.

WHAT YOU NEED

npn transistor (2N3053 or BFY51); diode (OA91); resistors – 100Ω (brown black brown), 1 kΩ (brown black red), 10 kΩ (brown black orange); potentiometer 10 kΩ; two lamps (6 V 0.06 A) and holders; battery 4.5 V; S-DeC; tinned copper wire 22 gauge; 1 mm and 2 mm bore plastic (or rubber) sleeving.

(A) LIGHTING A LAMP

One layout for the circuit is shown. Connect it. If all is well lamp L_1 should light up but it will not be fully bright because you are using a 4.5 V battery to light a 6 V lamp.

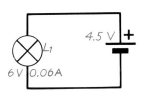

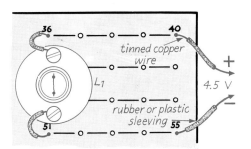

(B) A SERIES CIRCUIT

In series means one-after-the-other. In this circuit L_1 and L_2 are both dimmer than in **A**. See what happens when L_2 is unscrewed from its holder.

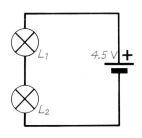

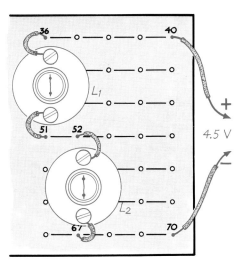

9

(C) WHAT A RESISTOR DOES

First use a $100\,\Omega$ resistor for R_1. L_1 will be dimmer than in **A** because R_1 has reduced the current. Now use a $1\,k\Omega$ resistor for R_1; it makes the current too small to light L_1 even dimly.

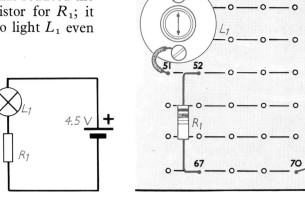

Make a 'dimmer' circuit by using a $10\,k\Omega$ potentiometer for R_1. Take leads from one *end* lug and the *centre* lug of the potentiometer to holes 52 and 67 on the S-DeC. (See page 6 for making 'joints'.) Rotate the spindle slowly, first one way then right round to the other end; L_1 should get dimmer and brighter.

(D) WHAT A DIODE DOES

You can use the same layout as in **C** but with the diode D_1 replacing R_1 in holes 52 and 67. L_1 lights with D_1 connected one way round but not the other way.

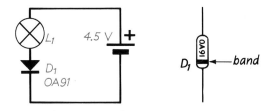

(E) A PARALLEL CIRCUIT

In parallel means side-by-side. L_1 and L_2 should both light up. See what happens when L_2 is unscrewed from its holder.

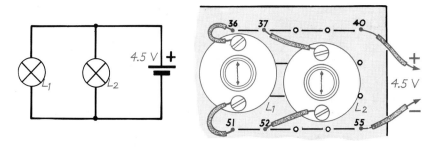

10

(F) WHAT A TRANSISTOR DOES

1 Before you start, check that the case of the transistor is marked '2N3053' or 'BFY51'. Identify the emitter lead (e), the base lead (b) and the collector lead (c).

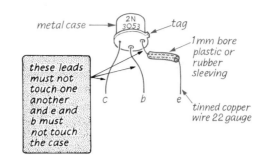

2 Lengthen the emitter lead so that the transistor can be mounted on the S-DeC in the holes shown on the layout. *Do not bend the leads too close to the bottom of the transistor* or they may break off in time.

Alternatively you could lengthen all three leads. None of them then needs to be bent but you must take care *not to push the lengthening wires too far into the sleeving* or they may touch one another or the metal case of the transistor and cause 'short circuits'.

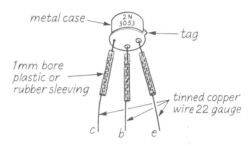

3 Build the circuit. After mounting the transistor *make sure its leads are not touching where they come out of the can*.

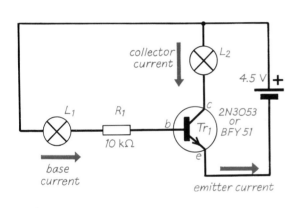

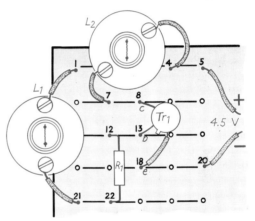

4 L_2 lights up but not L_1, showing that the collector current (which passes through L_2) is much greater than the base current (which passes through L_1).

5 Unscrew L_1 from its holder; the base current becomes zero and L_2 goes out. This shows that collector current only flows if there is some base current.

> In a transistor the base current (the input) 'switches on' and controls the much greater collector current (the output). A transistor acts as a switch and as a current amplifier.

2 PARKING LIGHT

A parking light for a car or a porch light can be switched on automatically as darkness falls by means of a photocell.

WHAT YOU NEED

Photocell (e.g. ORP12); two npn transistors (2N3053 or BFY51); resistors – $10\,k\Omega$ (brown black orange), $22\,k\Omega$ (red red orange); electrolytic capacitor $1000\,\mu F$; lamp (6 V 0.06 A) and holder; battery 4.5 V; S-DeC; tinned copper wire 22 gauge; 1 mm bore plastic (or rubber) sleeving.

ONE-TRANSISTOR CIRCUIT

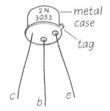

1 First check that the transistor is marked '2N3053' or 'BFY51'. Identify the emitter (e), base (b) and collector (c) leads.

2 Lengthen *either* the emitter lead *or* all three leads so that the transistor can be mounted on the S-DeC in the holes shown. (See page 5 for making 'joints'.)

3 Build the circuit, making sure after the transistor is mounted *that its leads are not touching one another where they come out of the case*.

4 L_1 should light up when the photocell is in the dark or is covered with a handkerchief.

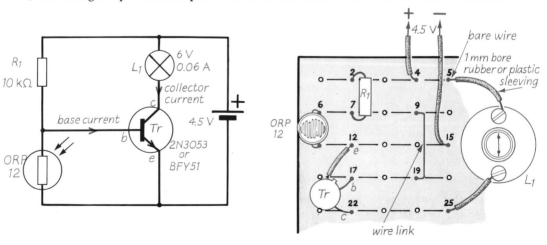

HOW IT WORKS

When light shines on the photocell its resistance is low (about $1 k\Omega$). Most of the current flowing from the positive of the battery through R_1 finds it easier to return to the negative of the battery by way of the photocell rather than through the base of the transistor. As a result, the base current is too small to cause a collector current which is large enough to light L_1.

In the dark the photocell no longer acts as a by-pass for the base current because its resistance is much greater (about $10 M\Omega$). Most of the current through R_1 is then forced to flow into the base of the transistor. The base current, though still small, is more than before and is able to 'switch on' a collector current that is big enough to light L_1.

TWO-TRANSISTOR CIRCUIT

This is a more sensitive circuit; it switches on the lamp for a smaller change of light level. The emitter of Tr_1 is connected to the base of Tr_2 and the two transistors are called a *Darlington pair amplifier*. Before building the circuit lengthen *either* the emitter lead *or* all three leads on the second 2N3053 or BFY51 so that it can be mounted in the holes shown.

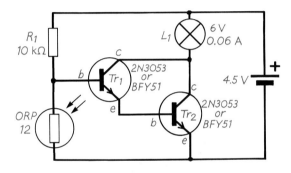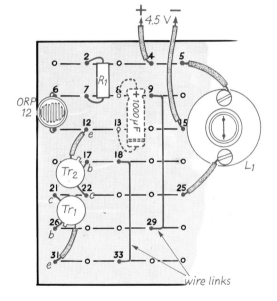

THINGS TO TRY

1 *Effect of R_1.* Change R_1 from $10 k\Omega$ to $22 k\Omega$. It now has to be darker before L_1 comes on.

2 *Delayed action light.* Connect a $1000 \mu F$ capacitor across the photocell (+ lead to hole 8, − lead to hole 13, as shown by the dotted lines). L_1 comes on more slowly in the dark because current that would otherwise flow into the base of the transistor, charges the capacitor. The base current therefore increases less rapidly.

L_1 also goes off more slowly if light (from the headlamps of a passing car, for example) falls on the photocell because the capacitor gives up its charge (discharges) and keeps the base current flowing for longer. Test this by having the photocell in the dark (L_1 on) and shining a flashlamp on it for a jiffy. L_1 should dim a bit but not go out.

3 *Light-operated burglar alarm.* Remove the capacitor. Swap round the photocell and R_1. L_1 should now come on in the light and go off in the dark. The circuit could be used to detect an intruder shining a torch or switching on a light in a room 'guarded' by the photocell.

3 RAIN DETECTOR

This circuit will let you know when it is raining. Your mother might find it useful when she has some washing hanging out!

WHAT YOU NEED

Two npn transistors (2N3053 or BFY51); resistors – 1 kΩ (brown black red), 3.9 kΩ (orange white red), 100 kΩ (brown black yellow); lamp (6 V 0.06 A) and holder; battery 4.5 V; S-DeC; tinned copper wire 22 gauge; 1 mm bore plastic (or rubber) sleeving; Sellotape.

HERE IS THE CIRCUIT

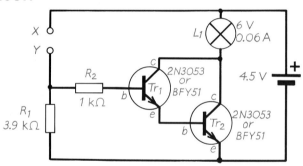

HOW TO BUILD IT

1 Check that the transistors are marked '2N3053' or 'BFY51'. Identify the emitter (e), base (b) and collector (c) leads.

2 Lengthen *either* the emitter lead *or* all three leads, on both transistors so that they can be mounted on the S-DeC in the holes shown. (See page 5 for making 'joints'.)

3 Make a rain detector 'probe' like the one below.

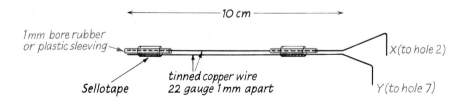

4 Assemble the circuit making sure after the transistors have been mounted that *their leads are not touching each other where they come out of the bottom of the transistors*.

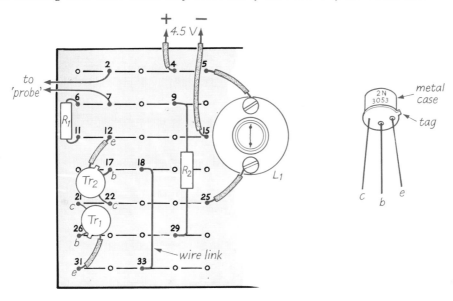

5 Put two or three drops of water on the probe so that they make links across the wires. L_1 should come on and give warning that there is 'moisture about'.

HOW IT WORKS

Water conducts electricity especially if, like rainwater, it contains dissolved impurities. When there is water between the two wires of the 'probe', current flows from the positive of the battery, through the water and R_2, into the base of Tr_1, out of the emitter of Tr_1, into the base of Tr_2 and out of the emitter of Tr_2 to the negative of the battery. The base currents 'switch on' the transistors and if the collector currents of both are together large enough, L_1 lights up.

The two transistors again make up a *Darlington pair amplifier*.

THINGS TO TRY

1 *Body-resistance measurer*. Replace R_1 by a $100\,k\Omega$ resistor. Remove the 'probe' and push two 10 cm long bare wires into holes 2 and 7. Grip the ends of the bare wires, one in each hand. If L_1 comes on the electrical resistance of your body is low; otherwise it is high. You can make it low by wetting your fingers before gripping the wires. 'Sweaty' hands will also bring L_1 on.

2 *Water level indicator*. Bend the ends of the bare wires from holes 2 and 7 over the edge of a glass, keeping them apart. Pour in water. When the level reaches the wires, L_1 comes on. You could use this circuit to tell you when your bath is filled to the level you want.

15

4
FIRE
ALARM

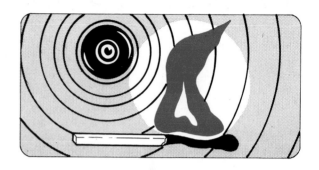

A thermistor can be used to give warning of temperature changes and operate an alarm. Here the alarm is a lamp, but in a fire control system, water sprinklers would be turned on automatically.

WHAT YOU NEED

Thermistor (e.g. TH3); two npn transistors (2N3053 or BFY51); resistors – 100 Ω (brown black brown), 1 kΩ (brown black red); potentiometer 10 kΩ; lamp (6 V 0.06 A) and holder; battery 4.5 V; S-DeC; tinned copper wire 22 gauge; 1 mm and 2 mm bore plastic (or rubber) sleeving; matches; ice.

HERE IS THE CIRCUIT

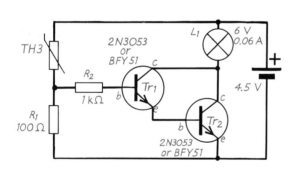

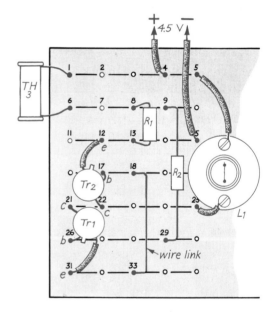

HOW TO BUILD IT

1 Check that the transistors are marked '2N3053' or 'BFY51'. Identify the emitter (e), base (b) and collector (c) leads.

2 If you have not already done so, lengthen *either* the emitter lead *or* all three leads on both transistors so that they can be mounted on the S-DeC in the holes shown. (See page 5 for making 'joints'.)

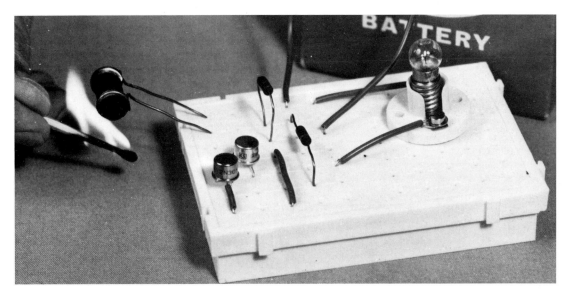

Warm the thermistor with a lighted match

3 Assemble the circuit making sure after the transistors have been pushed into the S-DeC that *their leads are not touching one another where they come out of the bottom of the transistors*.

4 Warm the thermistor with a lighted match: L_1 should come on.

HOW IT WORKS

The resistance of the thermistor decreases when it is warmed. The current flowing from the positive of the battery, through the thermistor and R_2 into the base of Tr_1 and then the base of Tr_2, therefore increases. If the increase is large enough the collector currents of both transistors are together sufficient to light L_1.

The two transistors form a *Darlington pair amplifier*.

THINGS TO TRY

Low temperature alarm. You will have to

    a remove the thermistor from holes 1 and 6 and mount it in holes 6 and 11,

    b remove R_1 from holes 8 and 13,

    c take leads from one *end* lug and the *centre* lug of a 10 kΩ potentiometer to holes 2 and 7. (See page 6 for making 'joints'.)

If you now rotate the spindle of the potentiometer *slowly* until L_1 *just* does not light up and then cool the thermistor by holding a small piece of ice (e.g. an ice cube from the refrigerator freezer) or something cool against it for a few seconds, L_1 should come on and give warning of a low temperature. *Take care not to get water on the S-DeC*.

The resistance of the thermistor increases when it is cooled. Can you explain how this circuit works?

5 FLASHING LAMP

A light is more likely to attract attention if it is flashing. Flashing lamps are used at road works and pedestrian crossings, on cars and as navigation lights.

WHAT YOU NEED

Two npn transistors (2N3053 or BFY51); resistors – 100 Ω (brown black brown), 1 kΩ (brown black red), two 10 kΩ (brown black orange); electrolytic capacitors – two 100 μF, 10 μF; two lamps (6 V 0.06 A) and holders; battery 4.5 V; S-DeC; tinned copper wire 22 gauge; 1 mm bore plastic (or rubber) sleeving.

HERE IS THE CIRCUIT

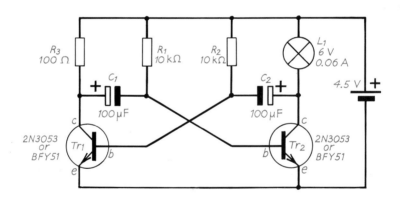

HOW TO BUILD IT

1 Check that the transistors are marked '2N3053' or 'BFY51'. Identify the emitter (e), base (b) and collector (c) leads.

2 If you haven't already done so, lengthen *either* the emitter lead *or* all three leads on both transistors so that they can be mounted on the S-DeC as shown. (See page 5 for making 'joints'.)

3 Assemble the circuit making sure that the electrolytic capacitors are the right way round

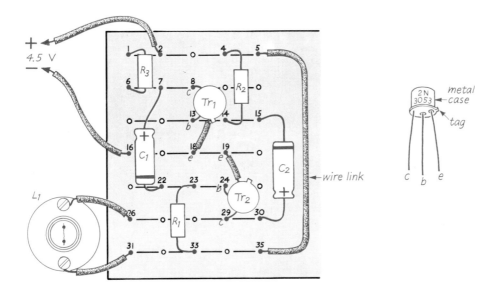

and *that the transistor leads are not touching each other where they come out of the bottom of the transistors.*

4 If all is well, L_1 should flash 30 to 40 times a minute and be on and off for equal times.

HOW IT WORKS

The lamp flashes because each transistor is switched on and off in turn due to C_1 charging and discharging through R_1, and C_2 doing the same through R_2. The flashing rate depends on the values of $C_1 \times R_1$ and $C_2 \times R_2$.

The circuit is called an *astable multivibrator*.

THINGS TO TRY

1 *Effect of C_1.* Change C_1 from 100 μF to 10 μF. L_1 flashes faster (about 60 times a minute) and is on for longer than it is off.

2 *Effect of C_2.* Make $C_1 = 100 \mu$F again, but change C_2 to 10 μF. The flashing rate will still be roughly 60 a minute but the on-times are shorter than the off-times.

3 *Effect of R_1.* Make $C_2 = 100 \mu$F again, but change R_1 to 1 kΩ. The flashing rate stays at 60 per minute but the on-time is greater than the off-time (as in **1**).

4 *Effect of $C_1 \times R_1$ and $C_2 \times R_2$.* Make $C_2 = 10 \mu$F leaving $C_1 = 100 \mu$F, $R_1 = 1$ kΩ and $R_2 = 10$ kΩ. The flashing rate is much faster and the on–off times are again equal. This is because $C_1 \times R_1 = 100 \times 1 = 100$, and $C_2 \times R_2 = 10 \times 10 = 100$.

5 *Two flashing lamps.* Change C_2 to 100 μF and R_1 to 10 kΩ. Replace R_3 by another lamp in holes 1 and 6. The lamps should flash one after the other as each transistor is switched on and off in turn.

6 MORSE BUZZER

You can use this to learn the Morse code.

WHAT YOU NEED

Two npn transistors (2N3053 or BFY51); resistors – 100 Ω (brown black brown), two 1 kΩ (brown black red), two 10 kΩ (brown black orange); disc ceramic capacitors – two 0.01 μF, two 0.1 μF; crystal earphone; loudspeaker, $2\frac{1}{2}$ in, 25 to 80 Ω; battery 4.5 V; S-DeC; tinned copper wire 22 gauge; 1 mm and 2 mm bore plastic (or rubber) sleeving.

HERE IS THE CIRCUIT

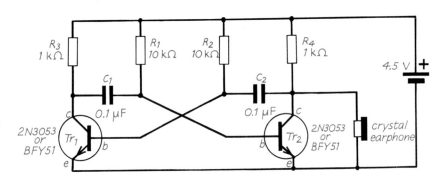

HOW TO BUILD IT

1 Check that the transistors are marked '2N3053' or 'BFY51'. Identify the emitter (e), base (b) and collector (c) leads.

2 If you haven't already done so, lengthen *either* the emitter lead *or* all three leads on both transistors so that they can be mounted on the S-DeC in the holes shown. (See page 5 for making 'joints'.)

3 Assemble the circuit making sure that when the transistors are mounted *their leads are not touching where they come out of the case*.

4 When you push the wire from the positive of the battery in and out of hole 2 quickly you should hear a 'dot' in the earphone. Leaving it in a bit longer will give a 'dash'. Now practise the Morse code.

It is better if you can get a Morse tapping key and
connect it between the positive and hole 2.

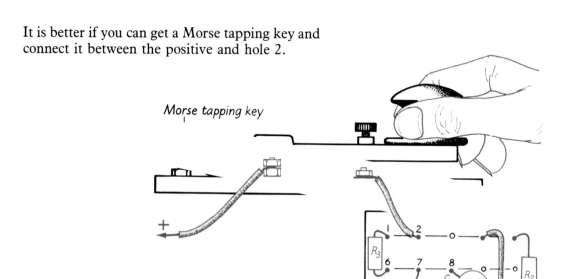

Morse tapping key

5 *The Morse code*

0 −−−−−	1 ·−−−−	2 ··−−−	3 ···−−	4 ····−	5 ·····
6 −····	7 −−···	8 −−−··	9 −−−−·		

A ·−	B −···	C −·−·	D −··	E ·	F ··−·
G −−·	H ····	I ··	J ·−−−	K −·−	L ·−··
M −−	N −·	O −−−	P ·−−·	Q −−·−	R ·−·
S ···	T −	U ··−	V ···−	W ·−−	X −··−
Y −·−−	Z −−··				

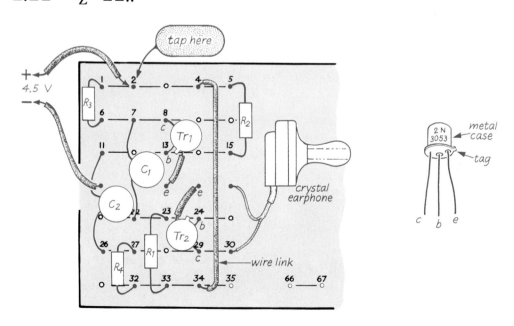

21

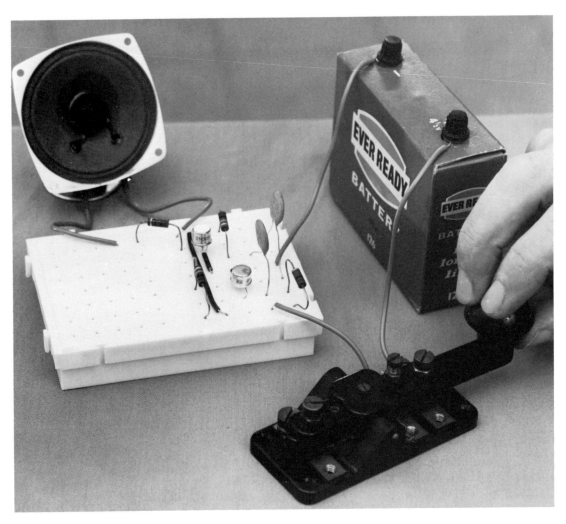

The complete kit, with Morse tapping key, assembled for loudspeaker operation

HOW IT WORKS

The circuit is an *astable multivibrator* similar to the one used in project 5 ('Flashing Lamp') except that the capacitors have much smaller values. This makes the transistors switch on and off too rapidly for a lamp to show the changes but the clicks they cause in the earphone occur so quickly that they produce a note.

THINGS TO TRY

1 *Effect of C_1 and C_2.* Change C_1 from $0.1 \mu F$ to $0.01 \mu F$. You should hear a higher note which becomes even higher if you also change C_2 from $0.1 \mu F$ to $0.01 \mu F$.

2 *Loudspeaker operation.* You will have to

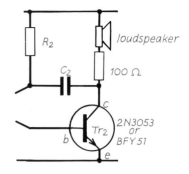

a change both C_1 and C_2 back to $0.1\,\mu$F,
b remove the earphone from holes 20 and 30,
c remove R_4 from holes 27 and 32,
d insert a $100\,\Omega$ resistor in holes 30 and 66,
e insert a loudspeaker in holes 35 and 67.

When you 'tap' now, the dots and dashes should be heard on the speaker.

3 Here is a 'message' in code. Work it out yourself first and then try it on your friends.

·— —/·—·/·—/··/—·/·/—·· ·—··/··/····/—/·/—·/·/·—· —·—·/·—/—·

—/·/·—··/·—·· ·——/····/—·· ··/··· —/·—/·——·/·——·/··/—·/——· ·—

——/·/···/···/·—/—··/· —···/—·—— ····/··/··· —/———/··—/—·—·/····

4 *Room-to-room working.* This needs the help of a friend who, like you, has built the loudspeaker version of the buzzer. If you lengthen the wires from your loudspeaker so that it can be put in the room with your friend, and if he does the same so that the loudspeaker connected to his buzzer is in the room where you are, then you can send messages to each other.

To hear what *you* are sending, connect your earphone to holes 20 and 28.

7 BURGLAR ALARM

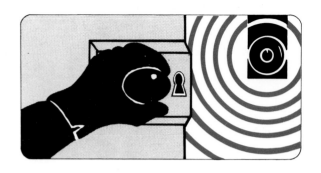

This circuit will tell you when an unwelcome guest enters another room at night and switches on a light. It could also be used to waken you at the crack of dawn!

WHAT YOU NEED

Photocell (e.g. ORP12); two npn transistors (2N3053 or BFY51); resistors – $100\,\Omega$ (brown black brown), $1\,k\Omega$ (brown black red), two $10\,k\Omega$ (brown black orange), $33\,k\Omega$ (orange orange orange); disc ceramic capacitors – two $0.1\,\mu F$; loudspeaker $2\frac{1}{2}$ in, 25 to $80\,\Omega$; battery $4.5\,V$; S-DeC; tinned copper wire 22 gauge; 1 mm and 2 mm bore plastic (or rubber) sleeving.

HERE IS THE CIRCUIT

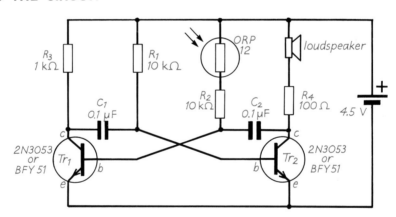

HOW TO BUILD IT

1 Check that the transistors are marked '2N3053' or 'BFY51'. Identify the emitter (e), base (b) and collector (c) leads.

2 If you haven't already done so, lengthen *either* the emitter lead *or* all three leads on both transistors so that they can be mounted on the S-DeC in the holes shown. (See page 5 for making 'joints'.)

3 Assemble the circuit (making sure that when the transistors are in the S-DeC *their leads are not touching where they come out of the case*) but do not connect the battery yet.

4 Cover the photocell *completely* with a handkerchief. Now connect the battery. A few 'clicks' may be heard in the speaker and then they should stop. If they don't it probably means that some light is still reaching the photocell. Remove your handkerchief and a warning note should come from the speaker, getting higher and higher.

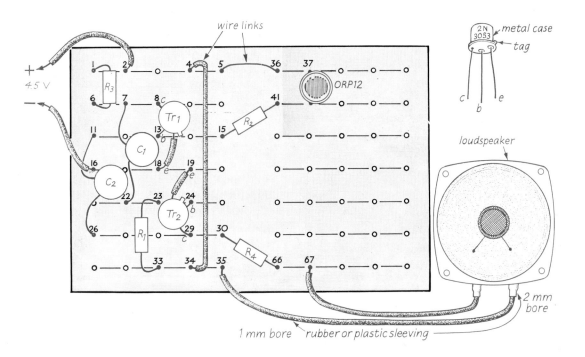

HOW IT WORKS

The circuit is an *astable multivibrator* like that used in the 'Morse Buzzer' (project 6) but in this case the rate at which the transistors are switched on and off is decided by the photocell. In the light, the photocell resistance is low and the switching speed is high enough to produce a note in the speaker. In the dark, the photocell resistance is very high and more or less stops the switching altogether.

THINGS TO TRY

1 *Effect of R_2.* Change R_2 in holes 15 and 41 from $10\,k\Omega$ to $33\,k\Omega$. The warning note will be lower.

2 *Water level indicator.* This is an alternative to the one in project 3 ('Rain Detector'). To make it you have to

  a make $R_2 = 10\,k\Omega$ again in holes 15 and 41,
  b remove the photocell from holes 37 and 42,
  c insert two 10 cm long bare wires in holes 37 and 42 and take them to a cup of water. When their ends are below the water level the loudspeaker should sound a warning note.

8
ELECTRONIC ORGAN

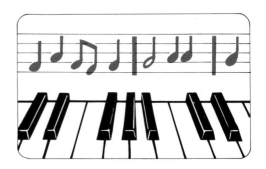

This is a chance to make your own electronic music.

WHAT YOU NEED

Two npn transistors (2N3053 or BFY51); resistors – 100 Ω (brown black brown), two 1 kΩ (brown black red), 2.2 kΩ (red red red), two 3.9 kΩ (orange white red), two 4.7 kΩ (yellow violet red), 5.6 kΩ (green blue red), 10 kΩ (brown black orange), 22 kΩ (red red orange); disc ceramic capacitors – two 0.1 μF; crystal earphone; loudspeaker 2½ in, 25 to 80 Ω; battery 4.5 V; S-DeC; tinned copper wire 22 gauge; 1 mm and 2 mm bore plastic (or rubber) sleeving.

HERE IS THE CIRCUIT

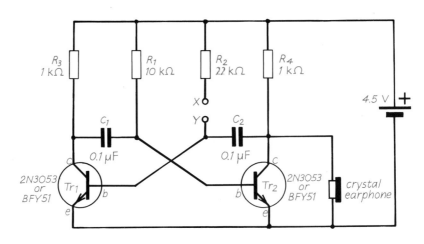

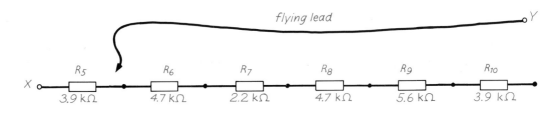

26

HOW TO BUILD IT

1 Check that the transistors are marked '2N3053' or 'BFY51'. Identify the emitter (e), base (b) and collector (c) leads.

2 If you haven't done so before, lengthen *either* the emitter lead *or* all three leads on both transistors so that they can be mounted on the S-DeC in the holes shown. (See page 5 for making 'joints'.)

3 Put the circuit together making sure that when the transistors are in the S-DeC *their leads are not touching one another near the case*.

4 Touch the flying lead on each of the seven wire links (the 'keyboard') in turn. They each give a different note. The lowest (*Note 7*) is given by the bottom link in holes 69 and 70 (most resistance); the highest (*Note 1*) by the link in holes 39 and 40 (least resistance). With a bit of luck you should be able to play something that resembles 'God save the Queen'. The 'music' for it is on page 29.

5 Connect another flying lead in hole 14. You now have a left 'hand' as well as a right to play on the keyboard. This should widen your repertoire.

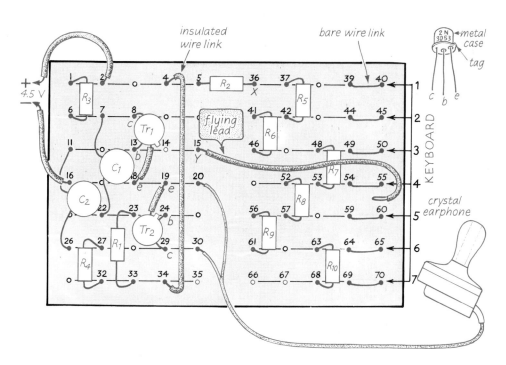

HOW IT WORKS

The circuit is an *astable multivibrator* like that in the 'Morse Buzzer' (project 6). The switching speed of the transistors, and so the pitch of the note produced, is decided by the position of the flying lead on the chain of six resistors (R_5 to R_{10}). For the highest note (the link in holes 39 and 40) the chain is not used at all.

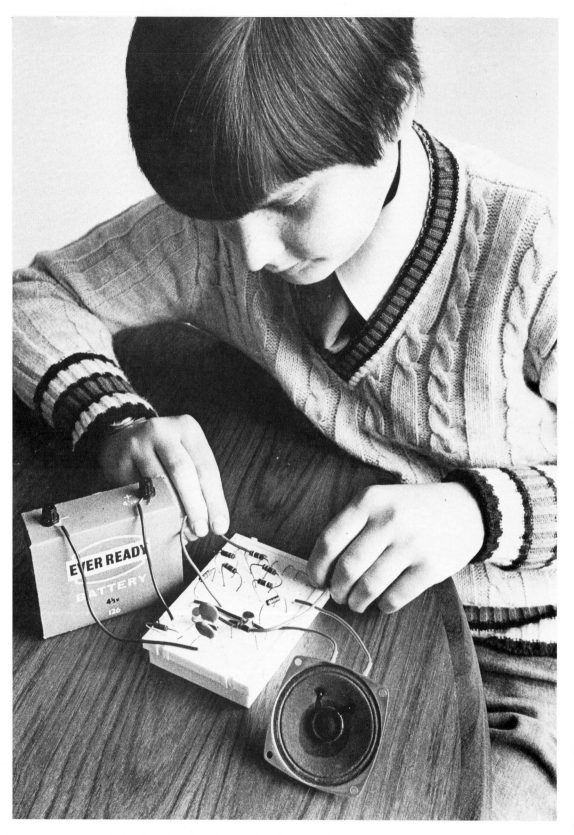

Electronic organ, with loudspeaker, showing two-handed operation

'Music' for 'God save the Queen'

The numbers tell you the notes to be played. *Note 1* is obtained by touching the wire link in holes 39 and 40, *Note 2* is given by the link in holes 44 and 45, and so on. When the numbers are close together you should play them quickly one after the other. When there is a star, make the note longer.

```
   6      6     5    7*            6 5
  God   save  our  gra  –  cious  queen
   4      4     3    4*          5 6
  Long   live  our  no  –  ble   queen
   5      6     7    6
  God   save  the  queen
   2      2     2    2*        3 4
  Send   her  vic  –  tor  –  ious
   3      3     3    3*          4 5
  Hap  –  py  and  glor  –  ious
   4     3 4   5 6   4*          3 2
  Long  to-o  reign  ov  –  er   us
  1 3    4*    5*     6*
  God   save  the  queen
```

THINGS TO TRY

1 *Loudspeaker operation* (with six notes). You will have to:

   a remove the earphone from holes 20 and 30,
   b remove R_4 from holes 27 and 32,
   c remove R_{10} from holes 63 and 68,
   d remove the wire link from holes 69 and 70,
   e insert a 100 Ω resistor in holes 30 and 66,
   f insert a loudspeaker in holes 35 and 67.

You can now 'entertain' your friends as well.

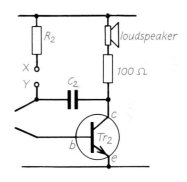

2 *Mystery tune.* Here is the 'music' for a well-known tune, play it and see if you recognize it – there are no prizes for the correct answer but it is a favourite with certain football supporters! When there is a star, make the note longer.

```
6 4 3 2*   6 4 3 2*
6 4 3 2   4  6  4  5*
4 4 5 6*  4  2  2 3
3 4 3 2   4  6  5  6*
```

3 *Two-tone siren.* Touch in turn with a flying lead, two wire links that are next to each other. Doing it quickly several times will give the familiar two-tone sound of a British police car and ambulance siren.

29

9 ELECTRONIC METRONOME

A musician uses a mechanical metronome to give the correct timing. In this electronic one, a loudspeaker produces the regular 'tick-tock' sound.

WHAT YOU NEED

Two npn transistors (2N3053 or BFY51); pnp transistor (ZTX500); resistors – 100 Ω (brown black brown), three 1 kΩ (brown black red), two 10 kΩ (brown black orange), two 33 kΩ (orange orange orange); potentiometer 10 kΩ; electrolytic capacitors – two 10 μF; loudspeaker $2\frac{1}{2}$ in, 25 to 80 Ω; battery 4.5 V; S-DeC; tinned copper wire 22 gauge; 1 mm and 2 mm bore plastic (or rubber) sleeving.

HERE IS THE CIRCUIT

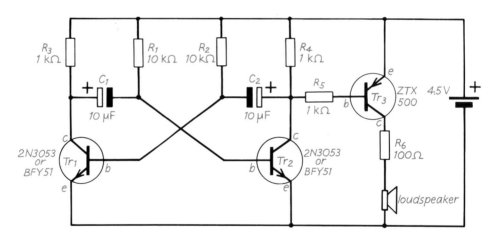

HOW TO BUILD IT

1 For Tr_1 and Tr_2 use 2N3053's or BFY51's; for Tr_3 use a ZTX500. Identify each transistor and its emitter (e), base (b) and collector (c) leads. The ZTX500 is a pnp type and must be connected with its *emitter to the positive of the battery*.

2 If you have not already done so, lengthen on all three transistors, *either* the emitter lead, *or* all three leads, so that they can be mounted on the S-DeC in the holes shown. (See page 5 for making 'joints'.)

3 Assemble the circuit making sure that when the transistors are in the S-DeC *their leads are not touching one another near the case*.

4 If all is well the metronome should work away merrily.

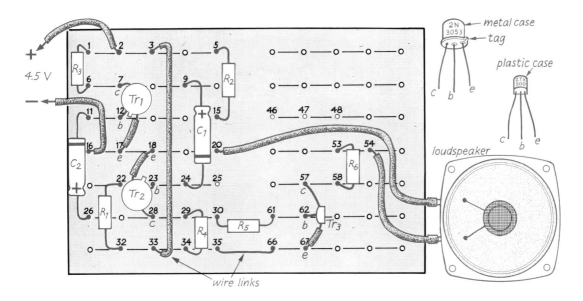

wire links

HOW IT WORKS

Tr_1 and Tr_2 form an *astable multivibrator* with a low switching speed, like the one in the 'Flashing Lamp' (project 5). They drive Tr_3 which is a loudspeaker amplifier.

THINGS TO TRY

1 *Effect of R_1 and R_2.* Replace R_1 by a 33 kΩ resistor; the 'tick-tocks' will be slower. If you also change R_2 to 33 kΩ they will be slower still.

2 *Variable speed metronome.* You will have to

  a remove R_2 from holes 5 and 15 and put it in holes 15 and 46,

  b remove R_1 from holes 22 and 32 and put it in holes 25 and 47,

  c connect leads to one *end* lug and the *centre* lug of a 10 kΩ potentiometer and push them into holes 5 and 48. (See page 6 for making 'joints'.)

When you rotate the spindle of the potentiometer the speed of the metronome will change. Adjust it to give 1-second 'tick-tocks'.

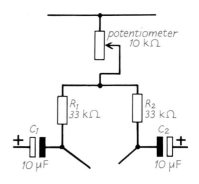

10
WAILING
SIREN

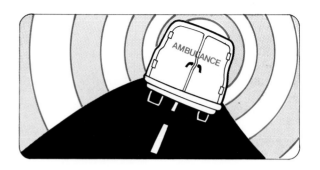

This circuit produces a note which gradually rises in pitch until it is steady – just like a factory siren.

WHAT YOU NEED

npn transistor (2N3053 or BFY51); pnp transistor (ZTX500); resistors – 100 Ω (brown black brown), two 33 kΩ (orange orange orange); disc ceramic capacitors – 0.01 μF, 0.1 μF; electrolytic capacitors – 1000 μF, 100 μF, 10 μF; loudspeaker 2½ in, 25 to 80 Ω; battery 4.5 V; S-DeC; tinned copper wire 22 gauge; 1 mm and 2 mm bore plastic (or rubber) sleeving.

HERE IS THE CIRCUIT

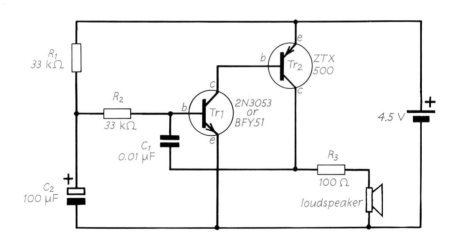

HOW TO BUILD IT

1 For Tr_1 use a 2N3053 or a BFY51; for Tr_2 use a ZTX500. Identify each transistor and its emitter (e), base (b) and collector (c) leads. The ZTX500 is a pnp type and must be connected with its *emitter to the positive of the battery*.

2 If you have not already done so, lengthen on both transistors, *either* the emitter lead, *or* all three leads, so that they can be mounted on the S-DeC in the holes shown. (See page 5 for making 'joints'.)

3 Assemble the circuit making sure that when the transistors are on the S-DeC *their leads are not touching one another near the case*.

4 When you connect the battery you will hear a note which rises to a steady pitch. If you now pull out one lead of R_1 from the S-DeC, the note falls but rises again when the lead is pushed into the S-DeC. When you carry on like this, pulling out one lead from R_1 for 3 seconds say, and then pushing it in for 3 seconds, the note rises and falls like a wailing siren.

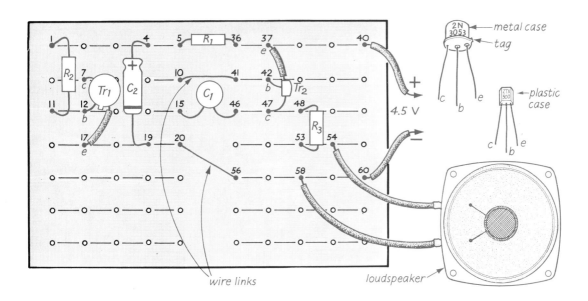

wire links   loudspeaker

HOW IT WORKS

The note from the speaker is caused by C_1 charging and discharging rapidly as the transistors switch on and off. C_2 controls the rate at which the process starts.

THINGS TO TRY

1 Replace C_1 by a 0.1 μF capacitor. A lower note is produced.

2 Keep $C_1 = 0.1\,\mu$F but change C_2 to 10 μF; the note rises faster.

3 Keep $C_1 = 0.1\,\mu$F but make $C_2 = 1000\,\mu$F; the note rises very slowly and you may think that it is not going to start at all.

11
AN
INTERCOM

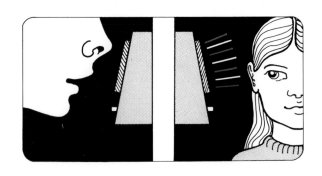

With this one-way intercom you can speak to someone in another room. A crystal earphone is used as a microphone.

WHAT YOU NEED

npn transistor (2N3053 or BFY51); pnp transistor (ZTX500); resistors – 100 Ω (brown black brown), 1 kΩ (brown black red), 4.7 kΩ (yellow violet red), 470 kΩ (yellow violet yellow); electrolytic capacitors – 10 μF, 100 μF; crystal earphone; loudspeaker $2\frac{1}{2}$ in, 25 to 80 Ω; battery 4.5 V; S-DeC; tinned copper wire 22 gauge; 1 mm and 2 mm bore plastic (or rubber) sleeving; 10 metres twin bell-wire (from local electrical shop).

HERE IS THE CIRCUIT

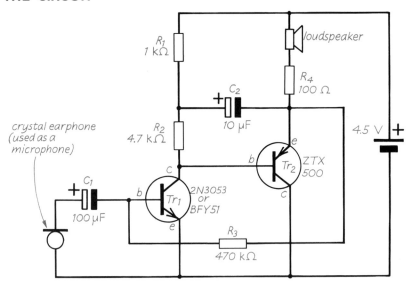

HOW TO BUILD IT

1 For Tr_1 use a 2N3053 or a BFY51; for Tr_2 use a ZTX500. Identify each transistor and its emitter (e), base (b) and collector (c) leads. The ZTX500 is a pnp type and must be connected with its *collector to the negative of the battery*.

2 If you have not already done so, lengthen on both transistors, *either* the emitter lead, *or* all three leads, so that they can be mounted on the S-DeC in the holes shown. (See page 5 for making 'joints'.)

3 Assemble the circuit making sure that when the transistors are mounted on the S-DeC *their leads are not touching one another near the case.*

4 When you connect the battery a 'plop' should be heard in the loudspeaker and if all is well a loud sound will be produced by tapping the 'microphone' with your finger.

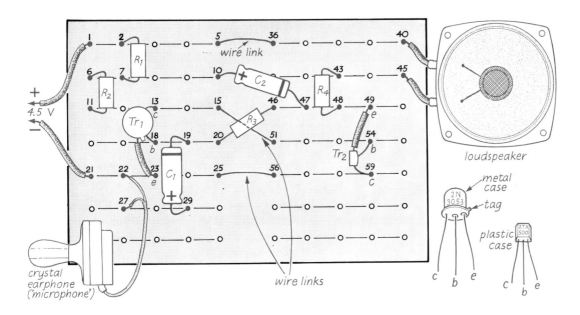

HOW IT WORKS

The 'microphone' changes sound into very small, changing electric currents which are boosted by the two-stage transistor amplifier before being fed to the loudspeaker.

THINGS TO TRY

Replace the loudspeaker in holes 40 and 45 by two long insulated wires, e.g. about 10 metres of twin bell-wire, connected to the loudspeaker in another room. Get someone to talk into the 'microphone' while you listen near the loudspeaker.

12 TWO TRANSISTOR RADIO

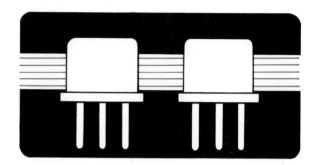

With a good aerial this radio receiver gives earphone reception on the medium and long wavebands.

WHAT YOU NEED

Two npn transistors (2N3053 or BFY51); diode (OA91); resistors – two 1 kΩ (brown black red), 10 kΩ (brown black orange), two 100 kΩ (brown black yellow); variable capacitor, 0.0005 μF; electrolytic capacitors – two 10 μF; disc ceramic capacitor, 0.01 μF; ferrite rod, 100 mm × 9 mm; crystal earphone; battery 4.5 V; S-DeC; knob; tinned copper wire 22 gauge; 7½ metres enamelled copper wire 24 gauge; 1 mm and 2 mm bore plastic (or rubber) sleeving; two rubber bands; 10 metres aerial wire (if TV aerial socket is not available) and crocodile clip.

HERE IS THE CIRCUIT

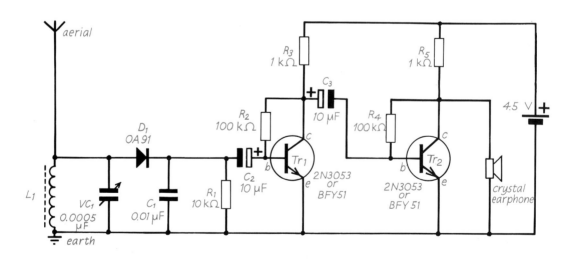

HOW TO BUILD IT

1 Check that the transistors are marked '2N3053' or 'BFY51'. Identify the emitter (e), base (b) and collector (c) leads.

2 If you haven't done so before, lengthen *either* the emitter lead, *or* all three leads, on both transistors so that they can be mounted on the S-DeC in the holes shown. (See page 5 for making 'joints'.)

3 Using 1½ metres of enamelled copper wire, wind a 50-turn coil on the ferrite rod. *You must scrape off* (with a penknife) *the dark reddish brown coating of enamel insulation from the ends of the wire* (so that the shiny copper can be seen) *where they are pushed into the S-DeC*.

4 'Join' 10 cm lengths of tinned copper wire to the lugs on the variable capacitor. (See page 6 for making 'joints'.) Slip 1 mm bore sleeving on each length, leaving 2 cm of bare wire at the end which will be pushed into the hole on the S-DeC. Fix the variable capacitor to the control panel and put on the knob.

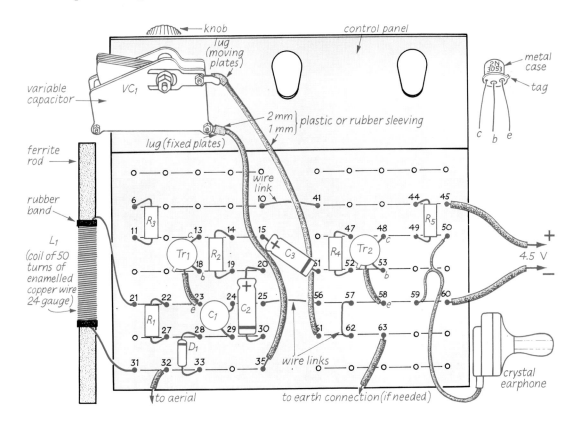

5 Assemble the circuit and slot the control panel into the S-DeC. Connect the wire from the fixed plates to hole 35 and the wire from the moving plates to hole 61. CHECK THE CIRCUIT CAREFULLY, making sure that *the transistor leads are not touching one another or the metal case*. Connecting the battery causes a 'crackle' in the earphone.

6 At home you can get good results using the TV aerial. Unplug the aerial cable at the back of the TV set (but leave the other end of the cable plugged into the aerial socket on the wall). Connect a wire from the central probe on the plug or from its metal casing (or from both), to the aerial hole (32) on the S-DeC.

If you can't use the TV aerial, a long wire (10 metres or so) will do, slung as high as possible indoors or outside. It must be insulated from whatever is supporting it at the far end. In this case an earth connection may also be needed, especially if you don't live near a radio

To tune in medium wave stations, slowly turn the knob on VC$_1$

38

transmitting station. You can make one by clipping a wire on to a water tap from the earth hole (63) on the S-DeC.

By *slowly* turning the knob on VC_1 you should be able to tune in medium wave stations (in Britain, Radios 1 and 5, and local radio). After dark more distant stations will come in (e.g. Luxembourg).

Note. If you hear 'whistling', putting R_2 into holes 9 and 19 (instead of 14 and 19) may get rid of it.

HOW IT WORKS

Read 'How Radio Works' on page 54. It will help you to understand the block diagram of the two transistor radio shown below.

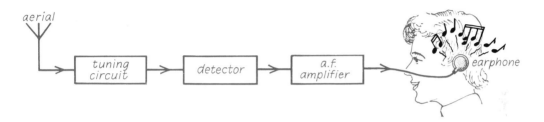

The tuning circuit is L_1–VC_1. Diode D_1 with C_1 and R_1 make up the detector. Transistors Tr_1 and Tr_2 with various capacitors and resistors form a two-stage audio frequency (a.f.) amplifier.

THINGS TO TRY

Long wave reception. Remove the 50-turn coil from the ferrite rod and using about 6 metres of enamelled copper wire, wind on a 200-turn coil. This will bring in stations on the long waveband (in Britain, Radio 4).

13
'CHIP' RADIO

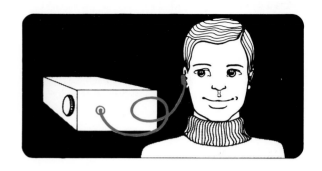

In many parts of the country this radio works from a ferrite rod aerial; no aerial wire or earth connection is needed. It has an integrated circuit (IC) which looks like a transistor but is a tiny 'chip' of silicon containing 10 transistors, 15 resistors and 4 capacitors. The 'chip' is nearly a radio on its own. With a few changes to the circuit it works a small loudspeaker.

WHAT YOU NEED

IC (ZN414 or ZN414Z); two npn transistors (2N3053 or BFY51); resistors – 330Ω (orange orange brown), 1 kΩ (brown black red), 4.7 kΩ (yellow violet red), 10 kΩ (brown black orange), two 100 kΩ (brown black yellow), 470 kΩ (yellow violet yellow); variable capacitor 0.0005 μF; electrolytic capacitor 10 μF; disc ceramic capacitors – 0.01 μF, 0.1 μF; crystal earphone; loudspeaker 2½ in, 25 to 80 Ω; ferrite rod 100 mm × 9 mm; knob; battery 4.5 V; S-DeC; tinned copper wire 22 gauge; 7½ metres enamelled copper wire 24 gauge; 1 mm and 2 mm bore plastic (or rubber) sleeving; two rubber bands; 2 metres aerial wire.

HERE IS THE CIRCUIT

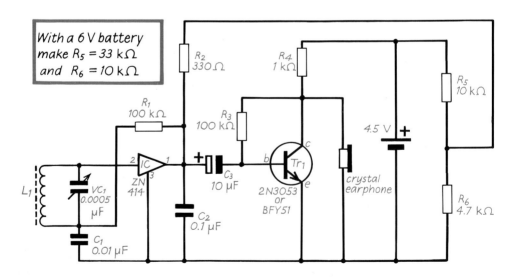

HOW TO BUILD IT

1 Check that the IC is marked 'ZN414' or 'ZN414Z' and the two transistors '2N3053' or 'BFY51'. Identify leads 1, 2 and 3 on the IC and the emitter (e), base (b) and collector (c) leads on the 2N3053's or BFY51's.

2 If you haven't done so before, lengthen *either* the emitter lead, *or* all three leads, on one transistor, so that it can be mounted in the holes shown. (See page 5 for making 'joints'.) Also lengthen the leads on the IC.

3 Wind a medium wave aerial coil on the ferrite rod as explained on page 37, 'How To Build It' 3.

4 Join leads to the variable capacitor as explained on page 37, 'How To Build It' 4.

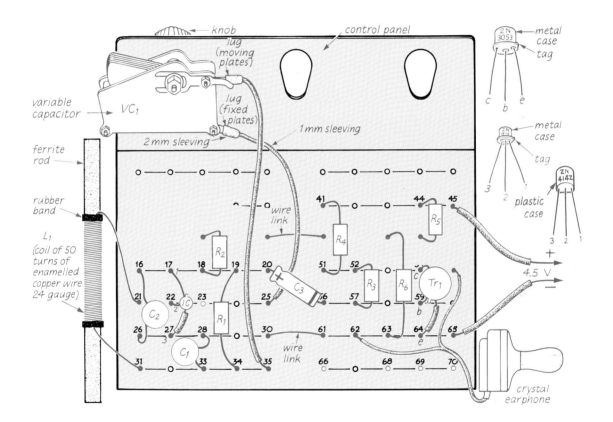

5 Assemble the circuit, not forgetting the two wire links. Slot the control panel with the variable capacitor into the S-DeC. Connect the wire from the fixed plates to hole 25 and the wire from the moving plates to hole 35. CHECK THE CIRCUIT CAREFULLY, making sure that *the transistor and IC leads are not touching one another or the metal cases*. When you connect the battery there should be a 'crackle' in the earphone.

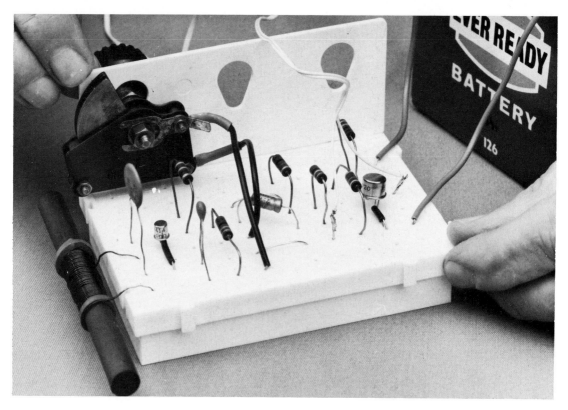

Slowly rotate the S-DeC for maximum volume

6 By carefully turning the knob on VC_1 you should be able to tune in medium wave stations (in Britain, Radios, 1 and 5, and local radio). *The ferrite rod aerial is directional, so slowly rotate the S-DeC for maximum volume.* If the signals are weak, try putting a 2-metre long aerial wire in hole 23 and fixing the other end as high as possible. If you live in a very poor reception area you may have to use the TV aerial (see page 38) to get good signals. After dark more distant medium wave stations (e.g. Luxembourg) can be received.

HOW IT WORKS

If you haven't read 'How Radio Works' (page 54), do so now. It will help you to understand the block diagram below.

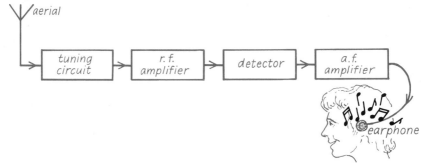

The ferrite rod acts as the aerial. $L_1–VC_1$ is the tuning circuit. The integrated circuit is both r.f. amplifier and detector. The 2N3053 or BFY51 transistor is the a.f. amplifier.

The IC needs 1.5 V only. It is obtained by having R_5 and R_6 connected in series across the battery and tapping off the required voltage from R_6.

THINGS TO TRY

1 *Long wave reception*. Remove the 50-turn medium wave coil from the ferrite rod and replace it by a 200-turn coil wound from about 6 metres of enamelled copper wire. You should now receive long wave stations (in Britain, Radio 4).

2 *Loudspeaker operation*. A second transistor Tr_2 is added and acts as a *Darlington pair amplifier* with Tr_1. To build the new circuit you will have to change the old one by:

a removing the wire from the negative of the battery from hole 65,
b removing the earphone from holes 55 and 62,
c replacing R_3 in holes 52 and 57 by a 470 kΩ resistor,
d moving the wire link from holes 30 and 61 to holes 30 and 66,
e moving R_6 from holes 48 and 63 to holes 48 and 68,
f replacing R_4 in holes 41 and 51 by a small loudspeaker,
g lengthening the collector lead on another 2N3053 or BFY51 (for Tr_2) and mounting it so that the collector is in hole 55, the base in 65 and the emitter in 70,
h inserting the wire from the negative of the battery into hole 69,
i connecting an aerial in hole 23 if it is needed.

Here is the circuit you should finish up with:

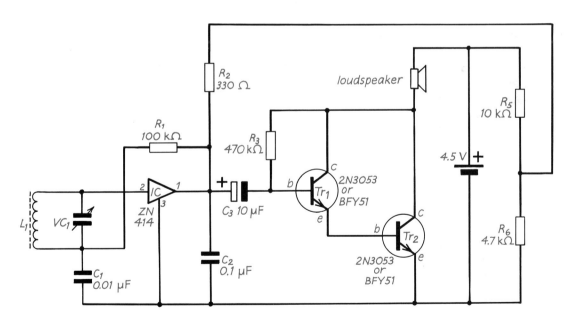

14
F.E.T.
RADIO

This radio is a bit tricky to tune, but once you get the hang of it you will find that not only does it bring in weak stations, it also separates closely spaced ones. It uses a field effect transistor (f.e.t.).

WHAT YOU NEED

Field effect transistor (2N3819); npn transistor (2N3053 or BFY51); resistors – two $1\,k\Omega$ (brown black red), $4.7\,k\Omega$ (yellow violet red), $10\,k\Omega$ (brown black orange), $100\,k\Omega$ (brown black yellow); variable resistor $10\,k\Omega$; electrolytic capacitors – $1\,\mu F$, two $10\,\mu F$; disc ceramic capacitor $0.1\,\mu F$; variable capacitor $0.0005\,\mu F$; crystal earphone; ferrite rod $100\,mm \times 9\,mm$; knob; battery $4.5\,V$; S-DeC; tinned copper wire 22 gauge; $7\frac{1}{2}$ metres enamelled copper wire 24 gauge; 1 mm and 2 mm bore plastic (or rubber) sleeving; two rubber bands; 2 metres aerial wire.

HERE IS THE CIRCUIT

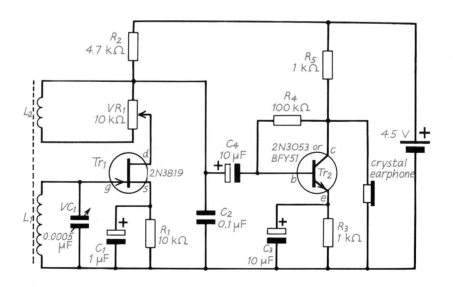

HOW TO BUILD IT

1 Check that the field effect transistor is marked '2N3819' and identify its source (s), gate (g) and drain (d) leads; they may be different if you bought it separately. Identify the emitter (e), base (b) and collector (c) leads on the 2N3053 or BFY51.

2 Lengthen the source lead on the 2N3819 and, if you haven't already done so, the emitter lead on the 2N3053 or BFY51, so that they can be mounted in the holes shown. (See page 5 for making 'joints'.)

3 Wind a medium wave coil on the ferrite rod as described on page 37, 'How To Build It' 3.

4 Join leads to the variable capacitor VC_1 as described on page 37, 'How To Build It' 4.

5 Connect two 10 cm leads to the *centre* and one *end* lug of the potentiometer VR_1. (See page 6 for making 'joints' to a potentiometer.) To the other *end* lug connect a 25 cm lead of insulated aerial wire.

6 Mount the parts on the S-DeC. Fix VC_1 and VR_1 on the control panel before slotting it into the S-DeC. Push the wire from the fixed plates on VC_1 into hole 24 and the one from the moving plates into hole 61. The lead from the centre lug on VR_1 goes into hole 17 and the other 10 cm one to hole 13. Wrap the 25 cm wire *twice* (fairly tightly) round the 50-turn coil on the ferrite rod and push its other end into hole 11. CHECK THE CIRCUIT CAREFULLY. You will hear a crackle in the earphone when the battery is connected.

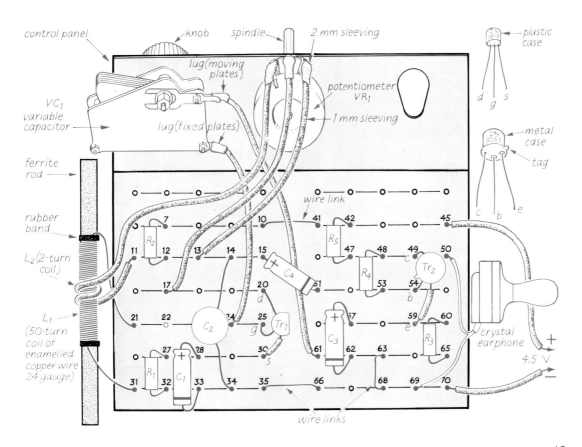

45

7 *Tuning the radio.* Connect a 2-metre long aerial in hole 22. Rotate the spindle on VR_1 to one end or the other, until you hear 'squegging' in the earphone – this is an unpleasant 'raspberry-like' noise. If you don't get it, remove the wire from hole 11 and unwind the 2-turn coil. Rewind it in the *opposite direction* round the 50-turn coil. 'Squegging' should now occur; turn back VR_1 carefully *until 'squegging' just stops*.

Now turn the knob on VC_1 *slowly*, until you hear a whistle, which drops rapidly in pitch and, as you keep turning VC_1 in the same direction, disappears before returning again. The whistle is caused by a station and you are tuned to it at the 'bottom' of the whistle where it disappears. Turn VC_1 back a little so that you are tuned exactly on the station. You may also have to turn back VR_1 slightly for the clearest reception. All this sounds difficult but it is not so bad once you get the idea.

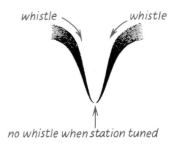

whistle   whistle

no whistle when station tuned

In Britain you should get Radios 1 and 5 and local radio and after dark some overseas medium wave stations. In good reception areas you will probably be able to do without a wire aerial and just use the ferrite rod as an aerial. You will then have to rotate the S-DeC for maximum volume since *the ferrite rod is directional*. Each station needs a different setting of VR_1 as well as of VC_1.

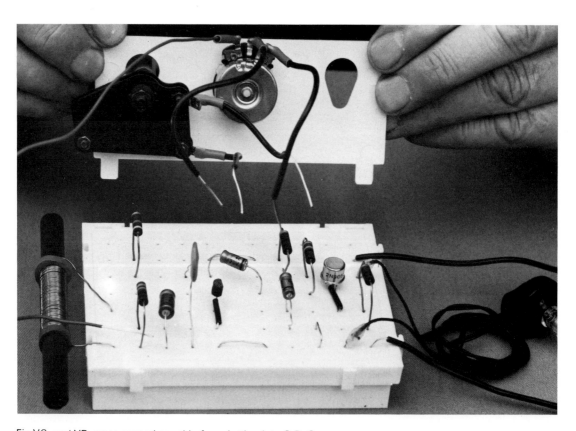

Fix VC₁ and VR₁ on to control panel before slotting into S-DeC

46

HOW IT WORKS

It is best to read 'How Radio Works' on page 54 if you haven't done so before. Tr_1 acts as an r.f. amplifier and detector: L_2 feeds back to L_1 some of the r.f. output from Tr_1 so giving even greater amplification. The feedback is controlled by VR_1. When the moving contact on VR_1 is near the top of the resistor, little or no current passes through L_2. If it is near the bottom, the current finds it easier to flow through L_2 than through VR_1 and the feedback is a maximum. Tr_2 provides a.f. amplification.

THINGS TO TRY

Long wave reception. Unwind the 2-turn coil L_2. Remove the 50-turn coil L_1 from the ferrite rod and replace it by a 200-turn coil wound from about 6 metres of enamelled copper wire. Rewind the 2-turn coil round the 200-turn coil. Now see if you can tune in any long wave stations, e.g. in Britain, Radio 4.

15 ELECTRONIC TIMER

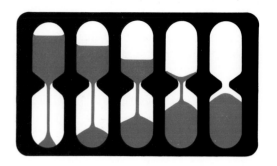

A lamp is switched on for a certain time when a contact is made momentarily. The circuit could be used as a photographic timer in a darkroom. It might also be arranged as a courtesy light which comes on, at the opening of a door or cupboard, for long enough to allow a particular job to be done.

WHAT YOU NEED

Two npn transistors (2N3053 or BFY51); resistors – 1 kΩ (brown black red), three 10 kΩ (brown black orange), 33 kΩ (orange orange orange); electrolytic capacitors – 100 μF, 1000 μF; lamp (6 V 0.06 A) and holder; battery 4.5 V; S-DeC; tinned copper wire 22 gauge; 1 mm bore plastic (or rubber) sleeving.

HERE IS THE CIRCUIT

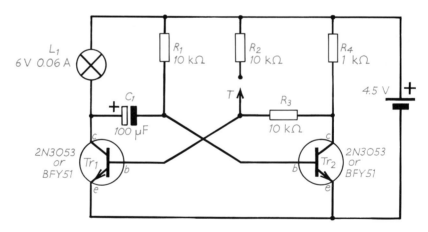

HOW TO BUILD IT

1 Check that the transistors are marked '2N3053' or 'BFY51'. Identify the emitter (e), base (b) and collector (c) leads.

2 If you haven't already done so, lengthen on both transistors, *either* the emitter lead *or* all three leads so that they can be mounted on the S-DeC as shown. (See page 5 for making 'joints'.)

3 Assemble the circuit making sure that *the transistor leads are not touching one another or the metal case where they come out of the transistor*.

4 Push the bare end (T) of the wire from hole 14 into hole 37 just for a jiffy. Lamp L_1 should come on for about 1 second.

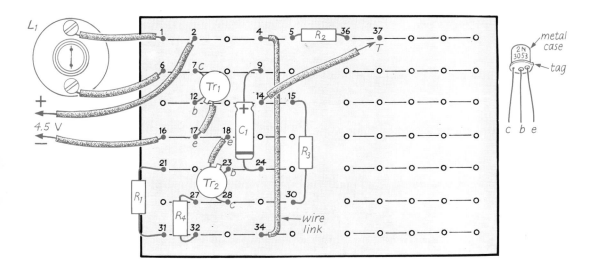

HOW IT WORKS

The circuit is another kind of multivibrator, called a *monostable multivibrator*. The astable multivibrator used in projects 5 to 9 doesn't have any stable states, that is, both transistors are switching on and off all the time. The monostable has one stable state with one transistor off and the other on. When the 'trigger' contact T is put in hole 37, the first transistor comes on and the second goes off, but only for a time which depends on the values of C_1 and R_1.

THINGS TO TRY

Effect of C_1 and R_1. Use a watch with a seconds hand to measure how long lamp L_1 comes on for when you make

    a $R_1 = 33\,\text{k}\Omega$ and $C_1 = 100\,\mu\text{F}$,
    b $R_1 = 10\,\text{k}\Omega$ and $C_1 = 1000\,\mu\text{F}$,
    c $R_1 = 33\,\text{k}\Omega$ and $C_1 = 1000\,\mu\text{F}$.

16 COMPUTER COUNTER

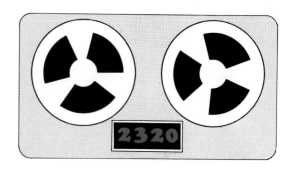

Computers count on a scale of two (binary system) using the numbers 0 and 1. Our everyday system is a decimal one working in tens. The circuit here is of a very simple binary counter.

WHAT YOU NEED

Two npn transistors (2N3053 or BFY51); pnp transistor (ZTX500); two diodes (OA91); resistors – three 1 kΩ (brown black red), two 4.7 kΩ (yellow violet red), two 10 kΩ (brown black orange); disc ceramic capacitors – two 0.01 μF; lamp (6 V 0.06 A) and holder; battery 4.5 V; S-DeC; tinned copper wire 22 gauge; 1 mm bore plastic (or rubber) sleeving.

HERE IS THE CIRCUIT

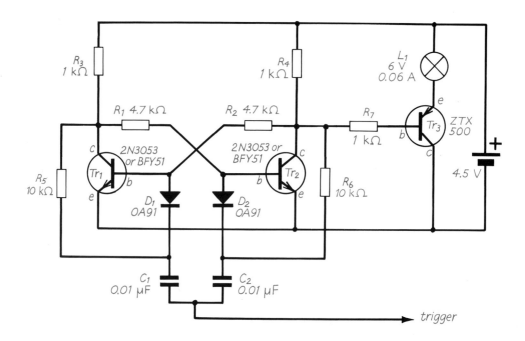

HOW TO BUILD IT

1 For Tr_1 and Tr_2 use 2N3053's or BFY51's; for Tr_3 use a ZTX500. Identify each transistor and its emitter (e), base (b) and collector (c) leads. The ZTX500 is a pnp type and must be connected with *its collector to the negative of the battery*.

2 If you haven't already done so, lengthen on all three transistors, *either* the emitter lead, *or* all three leads, so that they can be mounted on the S-DeC in the holes shown. (See page 5 for making 'joints'.)

3 Assemble the circuit making sure that when the transistors are mounted *their leads are not touching one another near the case. Also ensure that the two diodes are connected the right way round.*

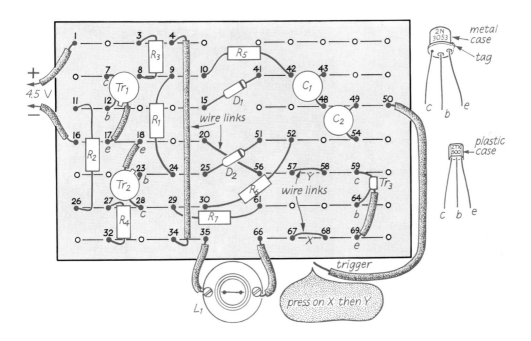

4 Send one electrical pulse into the counter by touching wire link X first and then wire link Y immediately afterwards, with the 'trigger' wire. Repeat the procedure a number of times so that several pulses are fed in. You will see that L_1 lights only on every *second* pulse.

When L_1 is off it means the count is '0', when it is on, the count is '1'. An actual counter has lots of circuits like this one connected together. One with twelve, counts to over 4000 – our very simple one only counts to 1! But see 'Things To Try'.

HOW IT WORKS

The circuit is a third kind of multivibrator, called a *bistable*.

It has two stable states. In one, Tr_1 is switched on and Tr_2 off. In the other, Tr_1 is off and Tr_2 on. The change from one state to the other is brought about by a 'trigger' pulse. L_1 shows the state of one of the transistors.

51

THINGS TO TRY

1 *Automatic pulses*. If you have a friend who also indulges in 'adventures with electronics' you might work with him and set up the circuit shown below. The 'Flashing Lamp' (project 5) should be reassembled on the right-hand side of the S-DeC. It sends pulses automatically to the counter (about one every second) if its output is connected to the 'trigger' input on the counter. You will then see that lamp L_2 only 'counts' every second flash of lamp L_1.

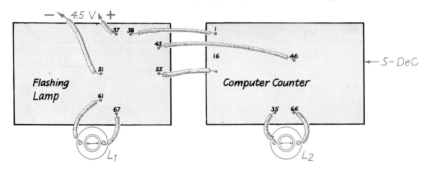

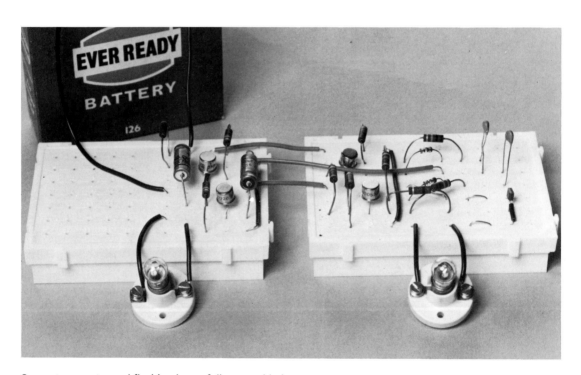

Computer counter and flashing lamp, fully assembled

2 *Binary counter to 7*. For this you need the co-operation of a third 'adventures with electronics' friend. He will have to build another 'Computer Counter' and connect its 'trigger' input to the output of the first counter as shown.

52

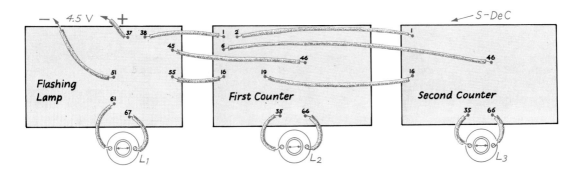

L_1 going on and off represents *two* pulses. L_3 comes on for *four* pulses and goes off for *four* pulses. The order in which the lamps light up is given in the table. '1' means the lamp is ON and '0' means it is OFF. If you know about binary numbers you will see that this arrangement counts up to 7, that is, 1 1 1 on binary.

Pulse number	L_3	L_2	L_1
1	0	0	1
2	0	1	0
3	0	1	1
4	1	0	0
5	1	0	1
6	1	1	0
7	1	1	1
8	0	0	0
9	0	0	1
10	0	1	0
11	0	1	1
12	1	0	0

HOW RADIO WORKS

DIRECT AND ALTERNATING CURRENTS

Direct current (d.c.) flows in one direction only. The current driven by a battery is d.c.

Alternating current (a.c.) flows first in one direction and then the other, i.e. it alternates. It starts from zero, rises to a maximum value in one direction, falls to zero again before becoming a maximum in the opposite direction and then rises to zero once more. In doing this we say the current passes through one cycle.

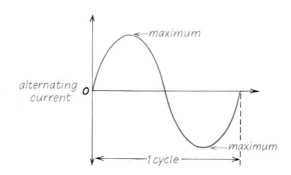

The number of cycles it makes in 1 second is called the *frequency*. The mains supply is a.c. and has a frequency of 50 cycles per second or 50 *hertz* (50 Hz). a.c. is produced by a dynamo (generator) and an electronic oscillator and plays an important part in radio and television.

AUDIO AND RADIO FREQUENCIES

Alternating currents with frequencies from 20 Hz or so to about 20 000 Hz (20 kilohertz=20 kHz) are called *audio frequency* (a.f.) currents because they produce a note we can hear when they are fed into a loudspeaker. In a microphone, speech, music and other sounds are changed into a.f. currents. For example middle C played on a musical instrument causes an a.f. current of 256 Hz in a microphone.

Currents with frequencies above 20 kHz are called *radio frequency* (r.f.) currents. They do not produce audible sounds in a loudspeaker but when they flow in an aerial they cause radio waves to be sent out into space. This does not happen with a.f. currents.

TRANSMITTER

In a radio transmitter a.f. current produced by the speech or music to be broadcast is 'combined' with r.f. current. The r.f. current comes from an electronic circuit called an

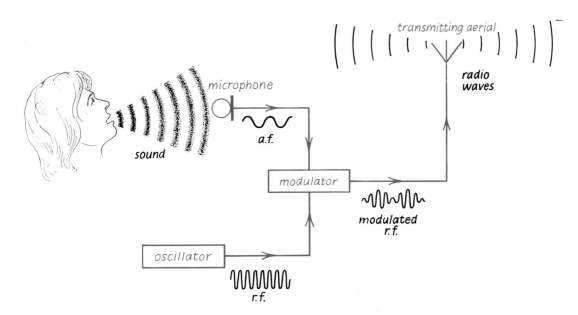

oscillator and, at first, is all of the same 'height'. In another circuit, called the *modulator*, its 'height' is changed by a.f. current from a *microphone*. When this modulated r.f. current is fed to the *transmitting aerial*, it gives rise to radio waves that travel into the surrounding space. The wavelength of the waves depends on the frequency of the r.f. current.

RECEIVER

When radio waves strike a *receiving aerial* they produce modulated r.f. currents in it that are smaller copies of those in the transmitting aerials from which they came. The *tuning circuit*

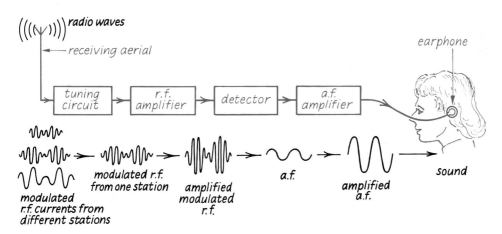

chooses one of the modulated r.f. currents from the aerial and the *r.f. amplifier* makes this one stronger. The *detector* separates the a.f. current from the r.f. and passes the a.f. on to the *a.f. amplifier* which boosts it so that the sound it produces in the *earphone* is loud enough to be heard.

55

TESTING TRANSISTORS

One reason for a circuit not working might be a faulty transistor. At some time it may have been connected wrongly by accident or the battery connections may not have been the right way round.

In the test circuits for npn and pnp types the *lamp will light if the transistor is O.K.* and go off when you remove the 10 kΩ resistor from the circuit.

Field effect transistors are less likely to be damaged because, with most of them, the drain and source can be interchanged but a simple test is given opposite.

1 *npn type* (2N3053 or BFY51)

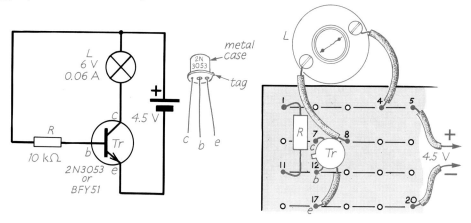

2 *pnp type* (ZTX500)

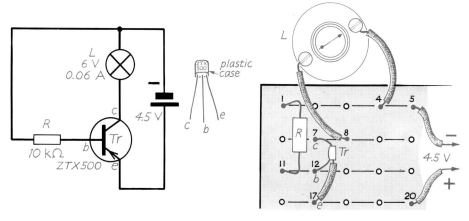

3 *f.e.t. type* (2N3819)

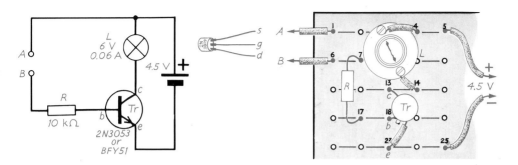

Hold wire *A* in contact with the gate (g). *L* should come on when wire *B* touches the drain (d) and then again when it touches the source (s). When wire *B* is held on the gate, *L* should *not* come on when *A* touches either the drain or the source. These results are summarized in the table below. (If you bought the 2N3819 separately the connections may be different from those shown here, so check when you get it.)

A to	*B to*	*L*
g	d	ON
g	s	ON
d	g	OFF
s	g	OFF

LIST OF PARTS

1	S-DeC
2	npn transistors (2N3053 or BFY51)
1	pnp transistor (ZTX500)
1	field effect transistor (2N3819)
1	**integrated circuit (ZN414 or ZN414Z)**
1	photocell, e.g. ORP12
1	thermistor, e.g. TH3
2	germanium diodes (OA91)
1	crystal earphone
1	loudspeaker $2\frac{1}{2}$ in, $25\,\Omega$ to $80\,\Omega$
1	variable capacitor $0.0005\,\mu F$ (Jackson Dilecon)
2	MES batten holders
2	MES lamps 6 V 0.06 A
1	midget linear potentiometer $10\,k\Omega$
1	ferrite rod $100\,mm \times 9\,mm$
1	knob
5 m	tinned copper wire 22 gauge (20 grams)

2.5 m	plastic (or rubber) sleeving 1 mm bore
0.2 m	plastic (or rubber) sleeving 2 mm bore
7.5 m	enamelled copper wire 24 gauge
10 m	aerial wire 1/0.6 mm tinned PVC covered
1	crocodile clip
2	rubber bands, small
1	battery 4.5 V, type 126
20	resistors, carbon, $\frac{1}{2}$ watt $100\,\Omega$, $330\,\Omega$, three $1\,k\Omega$, $2.2\,k\Omega$, two $3.9\,k\Omega$, two $4.7\,k\Omega$, $5.6\,k\Omega$, three $10\,k\Omega$, $22\,k\Omega$, two $33\,k\Omega$, two $100\,k\Omega$, $470\,k\Omega$
4	ceramic capacitors two $0.01\,\mu F$, two $0.1\,\mu F$
6	electrolytic capacitors $1\,\mu F$, two $10\,\mu F$, two $100\,\mu F$, $1000\,\mu F$

ADDRESSES

A complete 'Adventures with Electronics' kit can be bought from:
  Unilab Ltd, The Science Park, Hutton Street, Blackburn, Lancs. BB1 3BT
or perhaps obtained through local hobbies shops.

Firms supplying electronic parts are:
  Electrovalue Ltd, 28 St. Jude's Road, Egham, Surrey. TW20 OHB (catalogue available)
  Maplin Electronic Supplies Ltd, P.O. Box 3, Rayleigh, Essex. SS68LR (catalogue available)

Many firms advertise in *Practical Wireless*, *Everyday Electronics* and other magazines. A firm which does this is:
  Watford Electronics, 250 High Street Watford

If you have a local electronics shop you may find it worthwhile and more convenient to get parts there.

Beware of parts sold cheaply as 'untested' or 'manufacturer's surplus' or 'near equivalent to'; they may be sub-standard.

Schools and colleges can obtain supplies from:
  R.S. Components Ltd, P.O. Box 99, Corby, Northants. NN17 9RS (catalogue free)

S-DeCs are made by:
  Roden Products, High March, Daventry, Northants. NN11 4RZ